No 1 Sticker Scenes

First published in Great Britain 2013 by Farshore
This edition published in 2022 by Dean
An imprint of HarperCollins*Publishers*
1 London Bridge Street, London SE1 9GF
www.farshore.co.uk

HarperCollins*Publishers*
Macken House, 39/40 Mayor Street Upper,
Dublin 1, D01 C9W8, Ireland

CREATED BY BRITT ALLCROFT

ISBN 978 0 0085 3098 3
Printed in Poland
002

18
NIA

Meet Thomas, Emily, Nia, James, Percy, Rebecca and Gordon.

Who is your favourite?

Flynn has come to the Steamworks to check on the team's fire safety. All his friends are very pleased to see him.

STANLEY
SODOR STEAM WORKS

There's an emergency!
Thomas speeds to the
Search and Rescue Centre.
He wants to help the
rescue team.

on
and
on

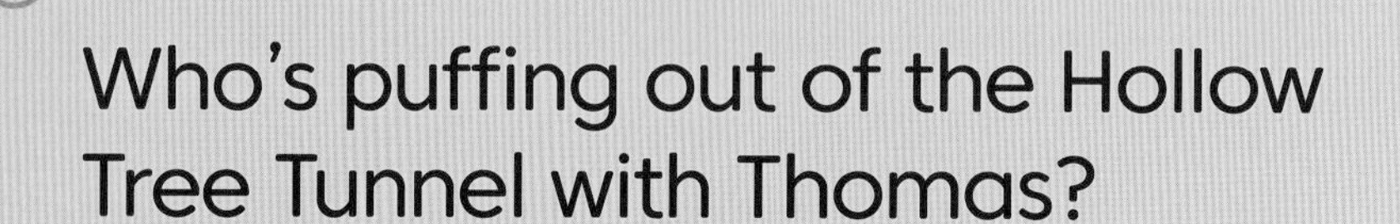

Who's puffing out of the Hollow Tree Tunnel with Thomas?

It's Hiro – he was stuck in the tunnel and Thomas has rescued him!

Use your stickers to show the two friends together.

Thomas arrives at the Town Hall just in time for a special music concert!
Show Thomas arriving at the Square. Then add the big brass band beside him!

The engines of the Blue Mountain Quarry are all hard at work! Everyone's very busy being useful.

Use your stickers to show the Narrow Gauge engines being Really Useful in the Quarry.
RHENEAS
2

Farmer Trotter has lots of animals on his farm! How many different farm animals can you think of?

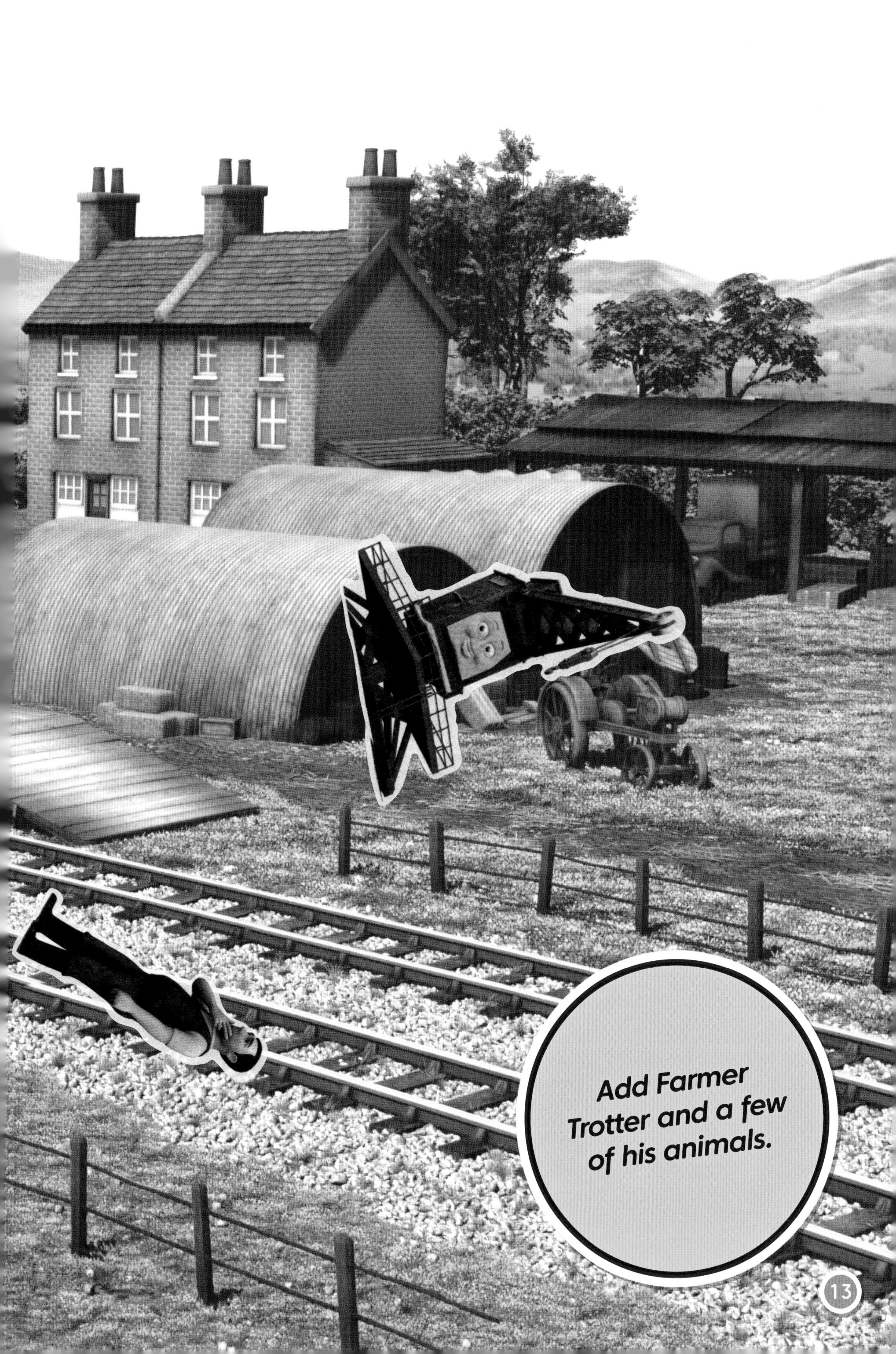
Add Farmer
Trotter and a few
of his animals.

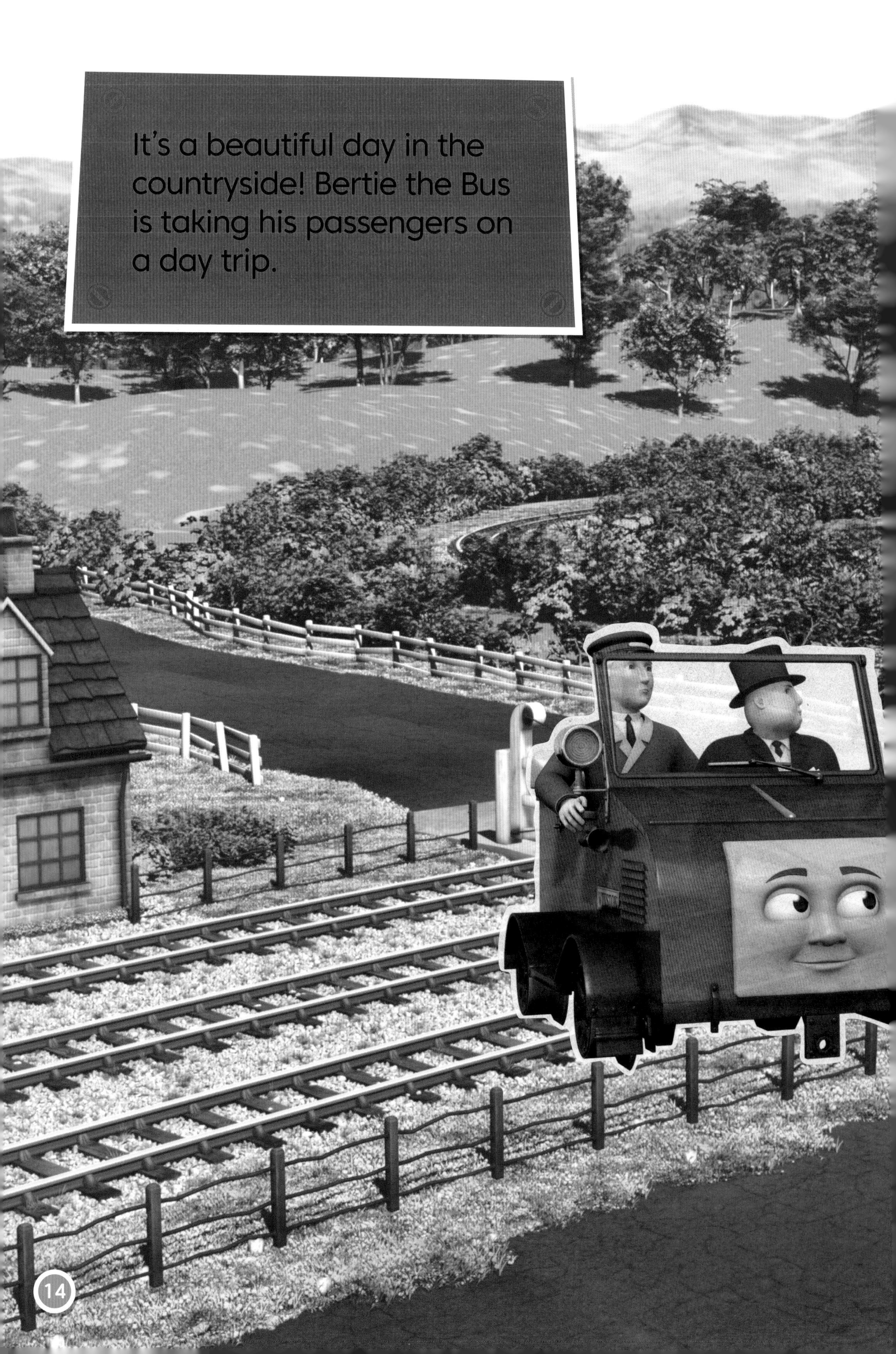

It's a beautiful day in the countryside! Bertie the Bus is taking his passengers on a day trip.

Show Bertie
on the level
crossing, and Flynn
waiting patiently
on the rails.

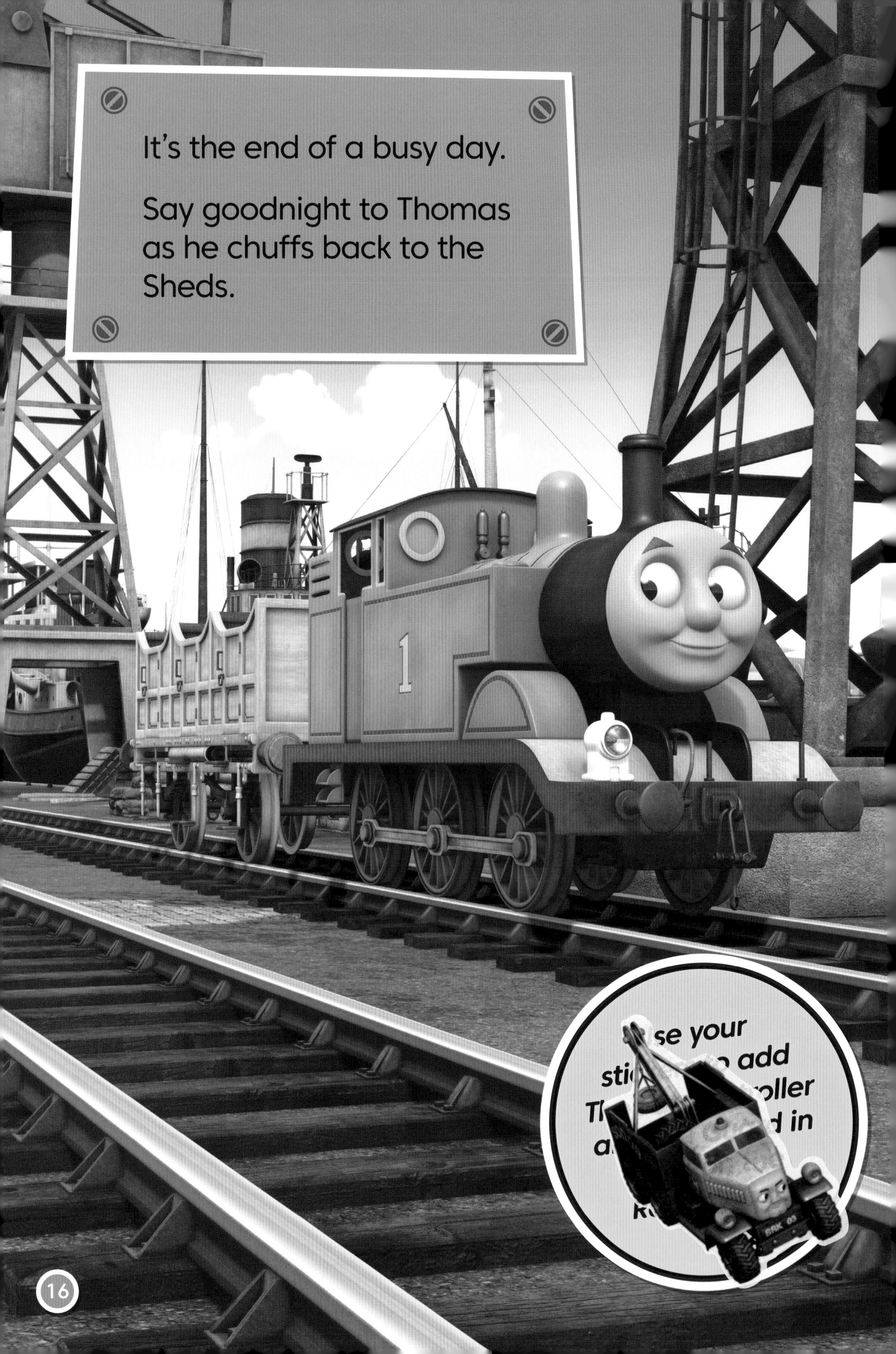
It's the end of a busy day.
Say goodnight to Thomas as he chuffs back to the Sheds.